RECITATIONS

COMIC AND OTHERWISE

BY

JAY HICKORY WOOD

AUTHOR OF
"THE CHRONICLES OF MR. POTTERSBY"

INCLUDING
"*THE CRICKET CLUB OF RED NOSE FLAT,*"
"*KICKING-STRAP'S RACE,*" "*McBRAE'S SYSTEM,*"
"*JELLICOE'S MELODRAMA,*" &c., &c.

WARD, LOCK & CO., LIMITED,
LONDON AND MELBOURNE

Printed in Great Britain by Butler & Tanner Ltd., *Frome and London*

CONTENTS

RECITATIONS:

COMIC AND OTHERWISE.

THE CRICKET CLUB OF RED NOSE FLAT

A YARN OF "OLE 'FRISCO."

I MET him at a cricket match—he came
    and sat by me,
And he chatted in a manner most agree-
    able and free.
He borrowed my tobacco, and he wasn't
    slow to ask
If I'd let him share my sandwiches, my
    matches, and my flask ;
And, in return, he told me some most
    interesting tales
About lassoing wild horses and harpooning
    monstrous whales.

He narrated fearful combats in the
    " Rockies " with a bear,
And blood-curdling scalping histories that
    nearly raised my hair ;
And, though, to all appearances he hadn't
    lost a limb,
Yet all these fearful incidents had hap-
    pened unto him.

Now, when a man identifies himself with
    certain acts,
It's very rude for any one to doubt that
    they are facts.
There are only two ways for it—you
    believe him, if you're wise ;
If you're not, and he is little, then you tell
    him that " he lies."

So, as my friend was taller than myself by
    quite a head,
And a toughish-looking customer, I swal-
    lowed all he said.
But when at last he paused for breath,
    and also for a drink,
I thought I'd change the subject, so I said,
    " No doubt you think
That cricket as a sport is very womanish
    and tame
Compared with scalping Indians. Do you
    understand the game ? "

" Do I understand the game ? " he said.
    " Wall, stranger, you may bet
What I don't know 'bout cricket—wall, it
    ain't invented yet.
Perhaps you ain't aware, my friend, that
    'way down Ole 'Frisco
We had a slap-up cricket club ? " I said
    I didn't know.

" Wall, now you know," he answered,
    " and I'll tell you 'bout a game
We played there just a year ago as warn't
    so plaguy tame."

2

And this is what he told me—of course it
    mayn't be true—
But as he told the tale to me I tell the
    tale to you :—

    .   .   .   .   .

" The boys 'way down in 'Frisco, though
    all a reckless lot,—
They'd most come out from England,—
    and had got a tender spot.
That spot it were the village green, where
    as boys they'd bowl and bat,
So we all made up our minds we'd have
    a club at Red Nose Flat.

We didn't have no captain—leastways we
    elected four,
But some one allus pistolled them, so we
    didn't vote no more.
You see, them captains allus tries to boss
    the blessed show,
Which ain't a healthy thing to do, 'way
    down in Ole 'Frisco.

Wall, we went ahead a-practising, as
    happy as could be,
Till Thunder Jack shot Blood-red Bill for
    hitting him for three.
And we held a general meeting, and we
    passed the following rule :—
'A member pistolled on the field by
    members, in the cool,
Providing he is up to date in payment of
    his " sub.,"
Is planted at the sole expense of this 'ere
    cricket club.'

3

CRICKET CLUB OF RED NOSE FLAT.

We heard as how a lot of chaps from
 Philadelphia
Was out on tour, so we challenged 'em to
 come along and play.
Our challenge was accepted, and one day
 they came around,
All ready for to play us, so we took 'em to
 the ground.

Joe Blazes says to me, says he, ' Ole pard,
 I'll tell you what,
There ain't a single shooting iron in all
 the blessed lot.
What do they mean a-coming here, ex-
 pecting for to win ?
It ain't half good enough, ole pard, a jolly
 sight too thin.'

They tossed for choice of innings, and you
 bet we won at that ;
We all was whales on tossing, and we
 started for to bat.
'Twas just as well we won the toss,
 because, I'm bound to say,
That even if we'd lost it, we'd have
 batted any way.

Wall, first of all I starts to bat, along o'
 Thunder Jack,
The bowler sends his ball along, I makes
 a mighty smack,
But, somehow, 'stead of hitting that there
 ball with that there bat,
I hits it with my leg. The bowler shouted
 ' How is that ?'

And that there blessed umpire started for
    to answer 'Out,'
When he saw my shooting iron—so he
    guessed there was a doubt ;
And he'd heard as how the batsman
    always got the benefit,
Which plainly showed as how that
    blessed umpire knew a bit.

You'd have thought as t'other umpire
    would have had some common
    sense,
But he went and said as Jack were out,
    on the following pretence :—
Old Jack had made a mighty swipe, and,
    if he'd hit the ball,
I guess we hadn't never seen that ball no
    more at all.

But, then, you see, he missed it, and his
    wickets they was downed
By the wicket-keeping chap, who said as
    Jack was out of ground,
And 'stead of speaking up and saying as
    there was a doubt,
The umpire said as Thunder Jack was
    very plainly out.

Then Jack he pulled his shooter out, and
    drew on him a bead,
And that there blessed umpire he went
    very dead indeed.
We shouted out 'Fresh Umpire,' but,
    somehow, no one came,
So we guessed we'd do without one, and
    we then resumed the game.

Wall ! after that they took to bowling very
    nice and slow,
And, if a fielder caught a ball, he allus let
    it go ;
So Jack and I, we slogged away as lively
    as could be,
Until my score was ninety-seven and Jack's
    was ninety-three.

Wall, we had to close our innings so's to
    give us time to win,
And, as they couldn't get us out, we said
    they might go in ;
They didn't seem so anxious for to bat as
    you'd have thought,
But we talked to them persuasive, and
    convinced 'em as they ought.

We told 'em as good cricketers should
    sooner die than yield,
And we loaded our revolvers, and we
    started out to field.
We'd Rifle Bill, a deadly shot, a-fielding
    near the rails,
And when Bill means to shoot a chap he
    very rarely fails ;

We'd Blazing Bob at cover point, and
    Mike was near the stand,
And Thunder Jack kept wicket, with his
    shooter in his hand,
And Lord ! them Philadelphy chaps, they
    couldn't bat a bit ;
I bowls 'em nice and easy just to tempt
    'em for to hit,

Then it came on me all like a flash, sir, as
    they was on the same game ;
And I sat on that 'oss all perspirin', and a
    prayin' as 'ow 'e'd fall lame.
Fifty yards, and a length to the good, sir !
    But I swore that the villains I'd baulk,
So I clenched my teeth tightly together,
    and I settled the 'oss to a walk.
Ah ! the 'oss were a beauty to walk, sir,
    there were no other 'oss walked so
    slow ;
But we was in front quite a length, sir, and
    we'd only a few yards to go.

Talk of excitement, my word, sir ! 'Twas
    those minutes as turned my 'air grey,
They was bound to gain on us at walking,
    but the question was if we could stay
Inch by inch, though they're walking their
    slowest, they're gaining, they gain
    more and more.
I speak to the 'oss. He knows what I
    mean, and he strains every nerve to
    walk slower.
The people are yelling like madmen, and
    among them I see the squire's face,
Deathly pale, and I shudder to think what
    it means if I win him the race.

" Now for it, my beauty, now for it ! Woa !
    steady, my boy, not so fast ;
Another ten seconds, my beauty, and not
    quite so quick as the last."
The 'oss struggled gamely to lose, sir ;
    closer finish, sir, never was fought ;
It wasn't his fault, nor yet mine, sir, but
    the distance to go was too short.

"Keep steady, my boy, and they'll beat
　　us." And slower and slower he
　　goes;
They're almost in front—can we do it?
　　Yes! No! We have won by a
　　nose!

But 'stead of smacking at the ball, they
    kept on looking back,
And seemed most interested in the ways
    of Thunder Jack.
One chap did hit a ball to leg, and started
    on a spurt,
But Rifle Bill just fetched him down, and
    he retired hurt.

Of course we beat 'em hollow; why, they
    never scored a run,
But they all admitted freely as it had been
    splendid fun ;
So we challenged 'em to come again, and
    play us a return,
And, p'r'aps it may be fancy, but they
    didn't seem to yearn.

However, we persuaded 'em to play it out
    next day,
But, when the morning came, we found
    as they had gone away.
We've challenged other clubs since then,
    but one and all they states,
As, they're very, very sorry, but they have
    no vacant dates.

So we swept the decks completely, and we
    calculated that
The boss of all the cricket clubs was ours
    at Red Nose Flat."

.   .   .   .   .

And this is what he told me—of course
    it mayn't be true—
But as he told the tale to me I've told the
    tale to you

KICKING-STRAP'S RACE.

You're lookin' at my old 'oss, sir, and
    you think he's a bit of a crock.
That 'oss were a racer once, sir, and I
    were a first-class jock.
Come down in the world? We 'ave, sir,
    we're down at the bottomest peg;
I've rheumatics in all my limbs, and the
    'oss is spavined in every leg.
Ah! Yes! But you ought to have seen us
    when we was both in our prime,
Just before the young squire's ruin! I can
    spin you the yarn if you've time.

The old squire 'ad been a scorcher. He'd
    lived at a terrible pace,
And, when he died, he left his son a heap
    of debts to face.
The young 'un took it right bravely,
    though; he'd any amount of pluck;
He was one of them 'opeful sort, sir, a
    chap as believed in luck.
They stripped his stables for 'im, sir, they
    cut down every tree,
To pay the old squire's debts, until he'd
    only this 'oss and me.

8

The 'oss were a flyer then, and I, well, *I*
    were a smartish lad
(Though I says it as shouldn't), and it
    grieved my 'art to see the young
    master sad.
But what could *I* do to 'elp 'im ? I wished
    both day and night
As I could be doin' somethin' to 'elp him
    out of his plight.
One day he comes into the stable with
    tears in his eyes (which was blue),
He says, " Bill ! Will you help us to land
    a good thing ? " I says, " Yes ! If I
    stands in it too ! "

" Agreed," says the squire. " Now, then,
    listen to me. I've enter'd this 'oss
    for the cup,
And if things goes wrong on the day of the
    race, the game will be just about up.
You ride him, of course ? " " You may
    trust me," I says. " I'll see as I lands
    'im 'ome fust."
" By Jove ! " said the squire. " But you
    mustn't do that," and he laughed till
    I thought he'd 'ave bust.
" I'm layin' *agen 'im*, you duffer, and mind
    you take care as we lose."
" All right, sir," says I. " You can leave
    it to me ; I can do with that 'oss
    what I choose."

The public they backed us right freely, for
    the 'oss 'ad a very good name ;
The squire got his book made to suit 'im,
    and no one suspected his game.

For they thought us above suspicion, sir,
    and though I don't care for to boast,
I'm sure there was no one suspected *me*
    as I rode to the starting post.
We all got away at the first attempt, and
    my 'art fair swelled with pride
To think as I 'ad the master's fate in *my*
    'umble 'ands to decide.

The other jocks let me break away, but
    was keepin' me well in 'and,
And I knew as all *I* 'ad to do was to keep
    my 'oss under command.
We'd gone 'arf a mile without change, sir,
    and I thought I'd ease up just a bit,
And let some one else take the running—so
    I started a pullin' the tit.
He slackened 'is pace in a minute, and I
    looked for the rest to ride past ;
But we still kept the lead, so I eased up
    some more, thinkin' p'r'aps as the
    pace were too fast.

And I kep' going slower and slower, but
    still we continued to gain,
So I gets a bit nervous, and looks round
    behind, and takes a big pull at the
    rein.
We was just 'bout a length to the good,
    sir. "Oh, hang it !" says I, "this is
    rot !"
We was getting quite close to the post, sir
    —so I pulls the old 'oss to a trot.
But when I looks over my shoulder,
    expecting them comin' on fast,
I sees 'em all trottin' behind me—and the
    last 'undred yards' post was past.

LITTLE BILL

By night, when all the world's abed,
Adown the street, with measured tread
Policeman X patrols his beat ;
His tread is measured, but his feet
Are measureless in size.   Their weight
At twenty pounds I'd calculate ;
At least, that's judging from his tread
As I can hear it in my bed.

While yet afar, the sleeping tramp
His tramp may hear, and quick decamp
The step's familiar, and he goes
To more secluded step to doze.

But see ! What's this he s haply found ?
A boy ? It is, in slumber sound.
Policeman X him roughly shakes ;
He shakes and shivers, then awakes.

" Now then, my cherub ! Up yer jumps !
Look lively, now ! Come, stir your stumps !
D'ye think you're settled for the night ?
Come, come, my lad, wake up ! That's
     right.
Now, off yer goes ! No standing still !
'Ere, what's yer name ? " " I'm little
     Bill."

THOUGHT-READING.

A HIGH-CLASS ENTERTAINMENT.

I PROPOSE to give you a few examples of Thought-Reading. Before doing so I wish you all to distinctly understand that I am but an amateur in the art, and have no desire to compete with the world-famed professors who have preceded me.

I must also apologise for being somewhat out of practice. Indeed, it is several years since I attempted anything of the sort. Consequently I fear that my entertainment may not be so good as I should like it to be. Years ago, when I was in full practice, my friends tell me that it was—worse. After seeing my entertainment to-night, you may find this statement difficult to believe.

The first essential for a Professor of Thought-Reading is a medium. Before choosing my medium I wish to state that I have no desire to deceive you in any way. In fact, I am quite incapable of doing so.

It would be an easy matter for me to ask any gentleman to come forward, and to have a carefully prepared confederate in the front row, ready to step on the platform before any one else had a chance.

I never descend to trickery of that sort. To be perfectly candid—I have brought my medium with me. Mr. Smith! kindly step this way!

Mr. Smith *steps on to platform.*

Now! In the interests of the audience, I must ask three *(three gentlemen rush on platform hurriedly and take their seats)*— three well-known and perfectly unbiassed gentlemen to act as committee. Any three *(sees committee).* Ah! There you are! Thank you! I will now proceed to blindfold my medium *(blindfolds medium)* not so much as a precaution, as to hide his face.

—Oh! By the by, I may as well mention that this entertainment is always most successful with a high-class audience. The more intelligent the audience the greater the appreciation—and applause. I mention this, not for my own sake, but because I never like to see an audience expose its own ignorance.

—The first experiment I shall try will be the reading of a number.

To Medium. Are you ready?

Medium. Yes!

—I am now thinking of a number. What is that number?

Medium. Six!

—That is quite right.

(N.B.—*The numbers here given need not*

be adhered to as the medium will be equally successful with others.)

—I will now attempt an even more difficult experiment.

To Medium. I am now thinking of nine numbers—all different. What are those numbers ?

Medium (slowly). Nine—eight—seven —six—*(quickly)* five, four, three, two, one.

—That is quite right ! Now, a great many people imagine that this feat is performed by means of electric communication between us. I assure you this is not the case. I will tell you how it is done. It is pure transference of thought from brain to brain. You see, as all scientists are aware, the brain is composed of a number of little cells, and this is—well—this is one of them.

(Sounds note on piano.) What am I touching now ?

Medium. The piano.

—Quite right ! What part of the piano ?

Medium. The key-board.

—Quite right ! Black or white notes ?
Medium. Yes !

—Quite right !

—I will now ask one of the committee for the temporary loan of some small article. My medium will tell you what it is ; further—he will tell you what it is *not*, a much more difficult feat, since there is only one thing that it *is*, while there are thousands of things it is *not*. I trust you follow me.

THOUGHT-READING.

(Borrows ordinary article from committee —for example, a watch.)

To Medium. Do you know what I hold in my hand?

Medium. Yes!

—Quite right! Is it a pound of butter?

Medium. No!

—No! Quite right! Is it a red-hot poker?

Medium. No!

—No! Quite right! You see, it's impossible to mislead him.

(N.B.—By a careful selection of similar articles—such as railway arches and torpedoes — the performer may make a good medium out of any intelligent, truthful person.)

To Medium. Is it a watch?

Medium. Yes.

—Yes! Quite right!

(N.B.—If the intelligent medium seizes on the first possible article he may rely upon being correct. The following feat may be achieved on the same system.)

To Medium. Can you tell me the time on this watch?

Medium. Yes.

—Quite right! Is it exactly midnight?

Medium. No.

—Is it exactly noon?

Medium. No!

—No! Quite right! Is it forty-seven minutes past nine in the evening?

Medium. Yes!

—Quite right! *(Hands watch to owner.)* Examine it for yourself, sir!

(Points at head of one of committee.)

To Medium. What am I pointing at?
Medium. A gentleman.
To Committee Man. Is that right, sir?
Committee Man. Quite right!

—Yes! Quite right! At what part of his head am I pointing?

Medium. His head.

(N.B.—*To succeed in this experiment, it is advised that the performer should have previously arranged with the medium as to these two answers. No further study is required.*)

—His head—quite right!

To Medium. Now, be very careful! How many hairs are there on this head?

Medium. One million, four hundred and sixty-two thousand, two hundred and two.

To Committee Man. Is that right, sir?
Committee Man. Quite right!

—Quite right! Of course if you feel any doubt on the subject, I shall be pleased to place your head in the hands of any respectable accountant, in order to verify my medium's statement.

—For my next experiment, I shall require one of the members of the committee to lend me a shilling. *(Committee leave platform hurriedly.)* Dear me! I trust that will prove to the audience that I am not in collusion with these gentlemen.

—Perhaps some gentleman in the audience will kindly lend me a shilling? *(Borrows one.)* Thank you, sir.

To Medium. Do you know what I hold in my hand?

Medium. Yes!

—Quite right! What is it?

Medium. A coin.

—A coin. Quite right! What is this coin made of?

Medium. Silver.

—Silver? *(to lender.)* Is that right, sir? Thank you! Quite right! What is the value of this coin?

Medium. Twelve pence.

—Quite right! What is on this coin?

Medium. There is a head on one side——

—Quite right!

Medium. And a tail on the other!

—Quite right! What is the date on this coin?

Medium. I don't know!

—Quite right! Now! To whom does this coin belong?

(Medium beckons performer to come nearer. Whispered colloquy — at end of which performer nods assent, pockets shilling, and advances to front of platform.)

—For my next experiment I shall require some gentleman in the audience to lend me a sovereign.

(N.B.—In the event of successfully securing this coin, proceed as before, and ask for a five-pound note. Continue until the patience and cash of the audience are exhausted, then exit hastily by a side door. In the event of the sovereign not being forthcoming)—

—I regret to say that, failing the loan of this trifling sum, I am unable to continue my experiments.

(Exit performer with shilling, pursued by medium and lawful owner of the coin.)

THE TRUE STORY OF LITTLE GEORGE WASHINGTON.

Some years ago there lived a boy, George
    Washington by name,
A thorough Yankee child was he and up
    to every game ;
His parents thought the world of him, he
    was his mother's pet,
His father said : "That child will lick
    creation, sir, you bet ! "
His maiden aunts adored him, he was
    uncle's only joy,
And all because he was a very, very
    truthful boy.

Now George he was a Yankee child, as I
    remarked before,
And learnt whilst very young indeed that
    two and two make four.
(I know you've all been much annoyed, as
    I was in my youth
By tales about this model boy who always
    told the truth ;
And so from motives of revenge I mean to
    have a try
And tell the truth about this boy who
    couldn't tell a lie.)

22

The art of popularity George very quickly
    found
Was humouring the weaknesses of every
    one around.
Whilst yet of very tender years the inno-
    cent young lamb
Committed burglary one day and stole his
    mother's jam ;
His mother, shocked at such a sign of
    villainy and greed,
Inquired of Georgie Porgie if he'd really
    done the deed.

With jam upon his pinafore, this very
    artful kid,
Who saw no way of getting out, replied :
    " Mamma, I did ! "
Instead of getting spanked as he deserved
    and also feared,
The family all hugged him till with jam
    they got besmeared ;
His father gave him fifty cents, and called
    him " Noble youth ! "
And all the neighbours flocked to see the
    child who told the truth.

Then Georgie thought the thing well out,
    and said : " Now, then, I guess
If these folks like confession I suppose I
    must confess ;
And as I can't confess unless I first
    commit a crime,
I'll be a little criminal, and own up every
    time."
He did all sorts of naughty tricks, and
    found it paid him well
To steal a pound or two of cake and then
    go home and tell.

But when he stole provisions—this was, I
    think, the worst—
He never owned up straight away, he
    always ate them first,
And when he stole the strawberry jam, the
    jam he loved the best,
He ate one half so that they might reward
    him with the rest.

In course of time it came to pass that
    Georgie older grew,
His parents and the family had taught
    him all they knew,
Which, added to the little facts that
    Georgie knew alone,
Was quite a little fund of information, you
    must own ;
But, still, 'twas very clearly time to edu-
    cate the boy,
And so he had to go to school—this
    mother's only joy.

When little George had been at school
    for p'r'aps a week or two,
He thought 'twas time to start and show
    the master what he knew,
He looked around for mischief for his
    little hands to do,
Until he spied a chestnut-tree that in the
    orchard grew.
" Ha, ha ! " cried little Georgie ; " I'll just
    chop down that tree,
And when I have confessed to it they'll
    give me jam for tea ! "

LITTLE GEORGE WASHINGTON.

He got a little hatchet; 'twas no sooner
    said than done;
The other boys were gathered all around
    to see the fun.
The master said: "Who did this deed?"
    George answered: "It was I,
And I'm the little boy who simply cannot
    tell a lie!"
And then he smiled his sweetest smile
    right in the master's face,
Awaiting, very patiently, the usual em-
    brace.

But then a thing occurred, which never
    had occurred before,
The master spanked young Georgie till he
    felt exceeding sore;
Instead of getting jam for tea he got no
    tea at all,
But fed on bread and water with his face
    turned to the wall!

So Georgie thought it out again: "It's
    clear it doesn't pay,
A thing may not suit 'B' although it's
    popular with 'A';
At home, where truth is popular, confes-
    sion is my rule;
There's always the alternative for me to
    use at school."

The incident to Washington a useful lesson
    taught,
And though he oft committed crimes, he
    ne'er again was caught;
For whene'er he broke a window and
    desired to get off free,

Ov course, we all got out to help the
    craythur ivery time ;

We used to tie him on behind when goin'
    down a hill

For fear we overtook him. He was best
    at standin' still.

That's why, at fires, we always sent a lad
    in front to say

They might expect us any time, for we
    was on the way.

We hadn't gone so far, before we shouted
    out " Bedad !

It's Mrs. Dooley's shanty, and the chim-
    ney's smokin' bad."

And, Mrs. Dooley, dacent soul, was
    standin' at the door—

We swore we'd save the woman's life, if
    we could do no more.

We didn't go inside, for fear the smoke
    would make us cough,

But we pumped on Mrs. Dooley till we'd
    pumped the water off,

Then Mrs. Dooley disappeared. She
    hasn't since been found,

And some there are who'll tell you they
    belave that she was drowned,

But we played upon her shanty till we'd
    washed it clane away,

And, where the pigsty used to be, there
    stands a lake this day.

We called on Pat O'Rafferty, and found
    the boy in bed,

So we woke him up and tould him he was
    just as good as dead,

And he climbed out of the windy, though
    he hadn't much to wear,

And then shinned down the water-spout,
while we came down the stair.

By this, the population was awake, and
shoutin' mad,

And throwin' out of windies ivery blessed
thing they had.

'Twas risky work for us below, but, with
undaunted heart,

We picked 'em up, and hid 'em safe
insoide the salvage-cart.

There were people sittin' on the roofs of
ivery house in town,

And so we threw up ropes to them, and
then we pulled 'em down.

We dived into their cellars—we were boys
that knew no fear—

And we saved ten jars of whiskey, and a
cask of bitter beer.

Then, when we reached the lawyer's
house, he asked us for a match

Bekase he was insured, and was afraid it
mightn't catch,

But he wouldn't stand us anythin', and so
we hung about

Until he'd got it well alight, and then we
blew it out.

Then we tried the " Pig and Whistle,"
though it hadn't got alight,

But we went inside the tap-room, to be
there in case it might.

They said there was no danger, but we
thought, at any rate,

As precautionary measure, we would play
upon the slate.

So, when we'd washed the slate quite
clean, and wiped off all the score,

myself liable for monies lost by persons who may bet on statements I have made in the past or will make in the future.

My greatest difficulty is my memory. It is, in many respects, a very excellent memory. Unfortunately, however, it is treacherous, and has often deceived me deliberately. On several occasions it has lured me into telling the truth while I have been under the impression I was lying in my most artistic manner. This sort of thing makes a man look ridiculous.

The two great obstacles to a thorough enjoyment of history are "names" and "dates." Far too much stress is laid upon these minor details.

For instance, if I choose to think of a man as "Richard," and you prefer to think of him as "John," I don't see that it matters at all. We don't change his identity. He's the same man still. If we want to talk about him, I shall know you mean "Richard" when you say "John," and you will know I mean "John" when I say "Richard." Very well then.

Dates are quite as unnecessary as names —that is, so far as history is concerned. I can quite see that a definite date affixed to a prophecy would increase the value of that prophecy very much indeed. But this is exactly where the ancient prophets missed their opportunity. They ignored dates. They prophesied events, but withheld the useful information as to when these events would take place.

The ancient historian, on the other hand, makes a feature of dates, which is very absurd of him. The events he records are all over—they *have* happened. We can't guard against or take advantage of them by knowing the exact date of their occurrence. The information is practically useless.

In my History, therefore, I have decided to ignore dates altogether. I shall, for my own guidance, name my characters, but any reader is perfectly welcome to think of those characters by names other than the ones I have bestowed upon them.

I believe in the liberty of the subject, and am, myself, the holder of a poetic license. I do not expect every reader to believe all the facts I shall lay before you. I recognise that they are too numerous and varied for the credulity of any single person.

Still, if each individual will select (according to his intellectual capacity) one or two of these facts, and believe them implicitly, a respectable aggregate of belief will be attained. The balance (consisting of statements that no hearer can swallow) I, myself, will undertake to believe, and the result will be incredible.

The Ancient Britons.

This trib were—as their name denotes —ancient Britons. They flourished about the year B.C.—or, to be strictly accurate, I don't know. They painted their bodies, and, unless it rained and the colours ran, looked very gaudy. They did not, however, paint their faces, as is the custom of the Ancient British ladies to-day.

The Queen of the Ancient Britons **was** Boadicea. I don't know why they called her that. I expect they had to call her something. Boadicea was very fond of farming. One day she was mowing **a** field of corn, when she heard that Julius Cæsar and a few friends from Rome had

NO. 1.

dropped in to see her. So she drove down on her mowing-machine to make them welcome. Unfortunately the horses ran away, and the Romans had to jump in a very lively manner to keep clear of the scythes. (See picture No. 1.)

This is Julius—up here—several feet above the others. He couldn't really jump any higher than the rest—but my artist had to distinguish him somehow, and he thought it would be inartistic to label him.

When the Romans had quite finished jumping, they settled down in the country and began to make roads. The Ancient Britons began to make tracks.

Then the Ancient Scotch poured down from the mountains, and overcame the Romans, who weren't used to it—I mean them.

So the Romans signed the pledge—and there arose a new dynasty.

The Early Saxons.

These were so called to distinguish them from the late Saxons, who had preceded them, and were then dead. History is silent as to the exact date they existed—at least, my History is. Silence is golden.

The Saxon King was named Canute. He was given this name in order to distinguish him from those whose names were otherwise. He was a very conceited man, and thought he could do anything he liked. One day he bet Alfred (who was next in succession) warm possets and cigars that he could stop the tide coming in. (See picture No. 2.)

Alfred took him, and went with him to see fair play. Here they are engaged in the unequal task. Alfred had the sense to come out when the water reached his chin, but Canute was just drunk enough to be obstinate. So he stayed where he was and was drowned. Alfred reigned in his stead, and—and—there was a new dynasty.

No. 2.

THE NORMANS.

The Normans are now in possession. In my desire to be accurate, I refrain from any explanation as to how they got there. There they are, and it is too late in the day to inquire into their credentials.

The first Norman was William I.—he was also the first William, as his name denotes. He ascended the throne on a given date, and died at a later period (see Macaulay's History). During the

36

interim—he reigned. On the day of his death he fell off his horse and the sagacious beast trod on him. The horse is a noble animal.

William 2nd succeeded him. By a curious coincidence, he began to reign on the same day his predecessor died. The

No. 3.

frequency of this coincidence in history has escaped previous historians—at least, if they have noticed it they have never mentioned it.

This monarch was very fond of hunting, and one day, while engaged in the pursuit with his chosen comrades, Wat Tyler, William Tell, and Robin Hood, they

I think I'll allow you to put your own construction on this picture. I *do* object to telling a falsehood—unless I know it to be one.

All I *do* know is—there was a fresh dynasty.

THE TUDORS.

The Tudors next demand our attention. At least, they don't really *demand* our attention—that is only my way of putting it. You needn't give them any attention, unless you like. They won't worry about it. They're all dead.

You will gather, from my calling them "Tudors" in the plural, that there was more than one. You are quite right. There were several, and they reigned at different times—successively—which means one after the other.

Henry VIII. married early—and often. He was very fond of his wife while she lasted, but she didn't last long, as a rule. The clergyman who had the contract to perform his marriage ceremonies grew wealthy on the fees. His name was the Reverend Cardinal Wolsey, and his last published remark was, "If I had only served my King as he has served me, he would never have lived to old age."

Passing over a few uneventful years, we come to the time of Elizabeth. That, of course, is a figure of speech. We can't come to it, because it's all over, and won't happen again.

Elizabeth was a Queen. She couldn't be a King, because she was a woman. She was

very brave. She defeated the Spanish
Armada by riding up and down on a white
horse while the English Navy sunk the
Spanish Fleet. (See picture No. 5.)

When I first saw this picture, I objected
to it. I told my artist that he had made
the Spanish Fleet too large and the English
Fleet too small. I said it was out of per-

No. 5.

spective. But he told me it was patriotism
to paint battle pictures that way, and that a
really patriotic artist didn't care anything
about perspective.

In this corner you may see Columbus
discovering America. He wasn't really
discovering America off the coast of

England, but we had a spare corner to fill up—and we thought we might as well put in Columbus as a lot of sky and sea that means nothing at all.

Oh ! by the by, Elizabeth was the first Englishwoman who wore stockings. A man gave her a pair as a present. *One* pair—only one—funny idea, wasn't it ? He might have given her two pairs—then she could have had one pair on and one in the wash. Well, never mind ! *She* died —and there was a new dynasty.

THE STUARTS.

The Stuarts came from Scotland. You inquire *why* they came from Scotland ? Well, I don't want to appear rude, but I am not going to tell you. I have my own reasons for not telling you. I am aware that my refusal may lead you to suspect that I don't know, but I would rather you suspected my ignorance than proved it. So we will pass on.

The first King was James—he sat on the throne for many years. I don't mean to say that he actually *sat* there for many years, because he had to get off and have his meals. That is merely an historical phrase. Towards the end of his life—he died, and his son Charles had so little respect for his memory that he started to reign right away—before the old man's funeral.

Charles had the making of a great statesman, and, if he hadn't lost his head —but that's a long story, and we needn't rake it up now. It's all over. Let bygones be bygones.

Oliver Cromwell came next. He wasn't a King—he was only a man. They nick-named him the "Boot-Protector," because he looked after the souls of the people.

This is a picture (Picture No. 6) of him

No. 6.

and his men looking for Charles II. Charles II. is up this tree—just here. My artist's difficulty is very plain. He has to let *you* see Charles, and, at the same time, has to make it apparent that the Boot-Protector doesn't see him. That is why he has drawn Cromwell and his men look-ing on the ground, as if they were search-

43

ing for a lost pin. About this time, some interesting events took place. I'm not sure what they were, and I don't think they'd interest you much. They're all over now, anyway. The most important was—there was a fresh dynasty.

THE ROYAL HOUSE OF HANOVER.

I don't think it would be very good taste for me to speak about the reigning dynasty. It's all very well to talk about dynasties that are dead and done with.

But the Hanoverians are with us yet—indeed, I am told that they are constantly arriving. So I think I will reserve my further historical remarks until—there is a fresh dynasty.

THE SULTAN OF JELHI.

THE Sultan of Jelhi was powerful and
    great,
A wilful, tyrannical, born potentate,
And he ruled as a ruler should rule o'er
    his state.

Sir Kenneth M'Tavish was Scottish, ye
    ken,
And most diplomatic, like all Scottish men.
He was Consul at Jelhi and Laird o'
    Cockpen.

Now the Sultan and Consul had got very
    hot
Over something or other, I can't tell you
    what,
But one said, "It is," the other "It's not."

They swore at each other in Scotch and
    Hindoo,
Till with passion their faces assumed a
    bright hue,
The Sultan went red and the Consul went
    blue.

Then the Sultan went home, and, to work
off his spleen,
He thrashed all his wives, of which he'd
nineteen,
While the Consul retired to write to the
Queen.

Now, Sir Kenneth he knew a few conjuring tricks,
In an amateur way, four or five, or p'r'aps
six,
And he thought that he saw a way out of
the fix.

He said, "I'll just give him one more
interview,
I'll show him of conjuring tricks one or
two,
And frighten that ignorant heathen
Hindoo."

So he wrote to the Sultan : "Perhaps you
don't know
Sir Kenneth M'Tavish is no common foe.
I'll meet you once more and to you I will
show

That Sir Kenneth M'Tavish, the Laird o'
Cockpen,
Is not to be reckoned with mere mortal
men,
He's a being that's far more than human,
ye ken."

THE SULTAN OF JELHI.

" Come on, then, you dog," said the dread
  potentate,
" You 'Shitan' from England, come on
  to your fate."
(Now "Shitan's" a word I decline to
  translate.)

Sir Kenneth M'Tavish proceeded to pack,
Stuffed a little aquarium right up his
  back,
And three ducklings, first gagging them
  lest they should quack.

He had three pounds of coffee and four-
  teen jam tarts,
With seven fresh cow-heels hid in various
  parts,
And a marked pack of cards, holding nine
  Kings of Hearts.

He'd three blacklead bullets, a pistol to
  shoot,
An electrical drum, a collapsible flute,
And a pound of fresh butter concealed in
  each boot.

Three miles of fine cotton he next wound
  about
His body, and then to the Sultan set out,
Appearing, it must be confessed, some
  what stout.

The Sultan, ensconced on his second best
  throne,
Received bold Sir Kenneth in private
  alone,
With haughty demeanour entirely his
  own.

The Consul proceeded to lay down the
   law,
But the Sultan remarked, "Allah kismet
   ben haw"
(Which is freely translated as "less of
   your jaw").

"Since greater than mortals you're claim-
   ing to be,
The first thing to do is to prove it to me,
Not through what I hear, dog, but through
   what I see."

"Very well," said Sir Kenneth, "then now,
   by your leave
I'll begin. You'll observe there is naught
   up my sleeve.
By this you will see I've no wish to
   deceive."

The Sultan remarked this could not be
   denied,
But said to himself, "El Bismillah! I've
   spied
This 'Shitan' from England is fullish
   inside."

Sir Kenneth then started to work with a
   will,
Performing his wonders with more or
   less skill,
Determined to give the old heathen a
   thrill.

He daringly shot himself right through
   the head
With bullets, not leaden, but made of
   black lead;
And, though to appearances killed, was
   not dead.

THE SULTAN OF JELHI.

He made bulky objects at once disappear
From his hand, and produced them again
    from his ear,
With many more tricks that I need not
    state here.

The Sultan remarking throughout, "Well,
    I'm blest,"
Or " I'm blowed," or " I'm jiggered," as
    though much impressed,
Yet chuckled inside him with marvellous
    zest.

His feats at an end, then the Laird o'
    Cockpen
Said, "Oh! Sultan of Jelhi, you now
    indeed ken
I'm far mair than human, above morta
    men."

The Sultan of Jelhi rose up with a choke
(Or a half-strangled chuckle), and solemnly
    spoke,
"Oh, Consul! I swear by my grand-
    father's moke,

Your magic is great, you're a foe I must
    dread,
You're a man to be feared by the living
    and dead ;
I bow to your might, place your foot on
    my head.

But e'er I do yield, grant one favour at
    least,
I've got some small magic I learnt in the
    East,
That is—to transform a man into a beast.

The test I would put you to you need not
    shirk,
On fellow-magicians my spell will not
    work,
It's only a small one I learnt from a
    Turk,

A mere mortal man it transforms to a
    beast."
"Come on with your test," said the Laird
    as he ceased,
"You won't frighten me, Sultan, not in
    the least."

The Sultan of Jelhi straight summoned
    his court,
And in came the courtiers, stout, thin, tall
    and short,
In full expectation of excellent sport.

The whisper went round that their terrible
    lord
Would practise some magic. With smiles
    very broad
They stood, courtier-like, all agog to
    applaud.

"You observe" said the Sultan, "I've
    naught up my sleeve.
By this you will see I've no wish to
    deceive,
This man in this room for ten minutes I
    leave,

One small incantation I say; when I've
    ceased
You retire. In ten minutes, or nine at
    the least,
You return, and the man is transformed
    to a beast."

The Sultan and courtiers then promptly
    retired,
The latter to wait till the time had expired,
The former to conjure the spell he
    required.

He touched a small spring, and there
    opened a door,
Which Sir Kenneth M'Tavish had not
    seen before,
Then every one heard a most blood-
    curdling roar.

A scream and a yell. As he peeped
    through a chink
The Sultan grinned hugely ; the courtiers,
    I think,
Exchanged 'mong each other a portentous
    wink.

Ten minutes is up, and they cautiously
    creep
To the room, ope the door just an inch,
    and then peep ;
No Consul was there, " but a lion asleep."

Then Ali Ben Houssan el Abomelik
Said, " Oh ! mighty Sultan, you've done
    this thing slick,
We hereby confess it's a mighty good
    trick."

" The next thing to do," said Mahommed
    el Ben,
" Is to take this Sir Kenneth, this Laird
    o' Cockpen,
And shut him, for safety, inside of a den."

Then the Sultan put down in his foreign
report,
"Diplomatic relations with England cut
short,"
And the Jelhians thought it uncommon
good sport.

A VISIT TO KNARESBORO.

THE following verses may appear confused to the casual observer, ut t hey
represent but faintly the confusion of
brain consequent upon visits to the " Cave
of Peter the Hermit," the " Scene of
Eugene Aram's Dream," and the " Petri-
fying Well."

To each of these places is attached a
history, which, being reeled off with great
rapidity by the guide, makes "confusion
worse confounded."

'Twas in the prime of summer-time
  When, from the Nag's Head Inn,
Drove twenty-four excursionists
  With sandwiches and gin.
All packed in one small waggonette
  Like sardines in a tin.

Away they drove with gladsome minds
  (The fare was half a crown),
To a public-house they came, and there
  They washed their victuals down,
While brightly shone the noon-day sun
  Over Knaresbro' Town.

And, as they rode, with one accord
　　They comic songs began,
Treating to chaff the passers-by
　　As only trippers can ;
But the driver sat above them all,
　　A misanthropic man.

His hat was well back on his head,
　　His face to sun exposed,
A surly look was in his eyes,
　　His lips were firmly closed.
Fresh air had made him very stout,
　　And red, and fiery-nosed.

He sat erect upon his box,
　　As stolid as could be,
Unheeding all their quips and jests
　　(So far as one could see),
As if hard fate had locked his brain,
　　And then mislaid the key.

He drove them moodily and fast,
　　And sharp the corners took.
Now up a hill, now down a hill,
　　Now past a purling brook.
And lo ! they saw an ancient dame,
　　Who hawked a little book.

" Now, mother, got some comic songs ? "
　　Inquired one saucy knave,
" What price ' Ta-ra-ra-boom-de-ay ? '
　　Come, can't you tip a stave ? "
The dame with cold and glassy eye,
　　Said, " This way to the cave."

A VISIT TO KNARESBORO'.

With hasty strides the trippers rushed,
   All curious and aglow,
The ancient dame close following,
   The dismal cave to show,
And down she sat among them all
   And told her tale of woe.

She told them of the holy man
   Who lit his fire with sticks.
She lightly touched on murd'rous deeds,
   Likewise contrived to mix
Poor Aram's dream with Houseman's
    bones,
   Then charged them one-and-six.

The trippers grumbled sore, but paid ;
   She took the coin, nor blushed ;
The trippers sadly turned to go,
   Confused and somewhat crushed,
When down the path, with hasty steps,
   The moody driver rushed.

" Ah, ha ! " quoth he, " you've heard the
    tale,
   Your faces show the sign.
She's charged you two, p'r'aps three-and-
    six,
   Or even three-and-nine.
You've heard of Eugene Aram's dream ?
   It's mild compared to mine !

" There's one hath done me grievous
    wrong,
   Ay, e'en yon ancient dame.
She's told that tale five thousand times,
   Without a blush of shame ;
I've heard it fifty times a year,
   And never twice the same.

" I've racked my brain from morn to
    night,
  I've read her penny guide,
To learn if Houseman murdered Clarke,
  Or if 'twas suicide ;
Or if 'twas ' Aram ' Eugene slew,
  And who it was that died.

" I tried to think why Houseman's bones
  Were found in Hermit's cave,
And why they saw tobacco smoke
  Ascending from his grave,
And why poor Eugene Aram died
  His wretched life to save.

" I dreamt I took that ancient dame,
  Who nightly at me girds ;
I took her to a lonely field,
  Where sweetly sang the birds ;
And there, beneath the open sky,
  I made her eat her words.

"And then she lay there at my feet,
  Choked by the awful pill ;
And as she lay it seemed to me
  That she was ' lying ' still.
There was a venom in her tale
  That choking could not kill.

" And then, beneath the dropping well,
  I hung her with her guide,
And watched them slowly turn to stone
  Till both were petrified.
And then, methought, I knew full well
  Who 'twas that really died.

A VISIT TO KNARESBORO'.

" And though 'twas nothing but a dream,
　Dispelled by morning's chime,
Oh ! gentle trippers, think of this
　Ere you condemn the crime.
I've heard that story twenty years,
　And diff'rent every time."

Throughout that night, till morning light,
　The trippers slumbered late.
Around them quilts of eider-down,
　Both warm and free from weight.
But round that driver's chest was strapped
　A waistcoat that was strait.

JELLICOE is a gifted author. He is also a confounded nuisance. He is a member of our club, and his entry is, as a rule, wonderfully coincident with the other members' departure. We don't object to his writing plays, but we do object to his reading them. He has a fertile imagination, and a brain which is simply chaos.

This combination results in the evolution of wild, weird plots, understandable by no man, and by Jellicoe least of any.

The other day he came into the club and found me asleep. He woke me up, of course. Then he produced a bulky roll of MS., and remarked that he was going to read me his new melodrama. I replied quietly, but firmly, that he was going to do nothing of the kind.

"May I explain the plot, then?" he pleaded.

I looked out. It was raining hard. The fire was bright, the room cosy.

"What will you have?" said Jellicoe.

That decided me. "Go on," I said; "explain it, if you can."

And he went on as follows : "There are forty-five characters in it. The reason I have so many characters is because of an arrangement I made with the manager of the theatre. He offered me a royalty of a sovereign either on each character or on each performance. I chose the characters as being more certain. These characters include one man who has lost his character and three servant-girls who never had one. First of all, there's the hero—at least, he isn't really a hero, but the play is written so that the audience think he is. I have worked it this way in case there should be an audience capable of thinking.

"The hero is a curate—that is, he is *really* a curate, but for the purposes of the play he is disguised as a butcher. He does this by dyeing his surplice blue. Being a hero, he spends most of his time in gaol. He is arrested every act, on false charges, and gets seven years' penal servitude for each offence.

"There are five acts, with an interval of seven years between each act. This gives the hero time.

"The heroine is a woman with a past ; she is also an unsocial problem. She doesn't care much who she marries, but she's madly in love with the villain— that's originality.

"The curate, who is also a butcher, forgets his sacred calling, and adores one of the servant-girls without a character. She returns his passion, having no use for it.

"The villain has committed seven murders; two of them he committed before the play opens, the other five he commits between the acts—one between each act. This saves bloodshed on the stage, and keeps it clean.

"The curate, being a butcher, is naturally suspected of these murders. This gives rise to a very strong situation in the third act, where the heroine says to the villain, 'Do your worst!' and the villain says he is doing. Then the curate's mother—I mean the butcher's mother—that is, the curate who's disguised as a butcher's mother—well, anyhow, she comes in and denounces the villain. She says, 'Thou art the man!' and he says he isn't; so the detective enters and arrests the curate, or rather the butcher—I mean the son of the curate disguised as a butcher's mother's denounced by her own son. It's a very effective curtain.

"The villain says to the mother, 'How camest thou here, and alive?' He asks this because he last saw her in Australia, dead. She says, 'It's a long story, and I'll tell you another time.' I worked it this way because I couldn't think of a reason myself. As a matter of fact, she never does tell him, but the audience think she will, so that comes out all right.

"Oh, by the by, the mother is a pawnbroker's widow—at least, she thinks she is, but she isn't, because he wasn't a pawnbroker—he was really a bishop, and he isn't dead. Nobody knows this but the audience, and they're not quite sure —that's artistic.

"Well, when the lost will is found in the heroine's pocket every one is surprised. Oh yes! about that lost will. You see, the heroine had a mother. She doesn't know she ever had, but it's pointed out to the audience in the first act, before they begin to go home.

"This mother is a woman of property— or, rather, a property-woman in a theatre. She cherishes a hopeless attachment for the pawnbroker, who's a bishop—this brings in the contrast between Church and Stage, and supplies the principal motive for the play.

"Well, she isn't dead, but she's made a will, and lost it. This will gets into the heroine's pocket. I have made a point of never explaining at all how it gets there, because that adds interest and excites and confuses the audience. Anyhow, this leads to some very fine dialogue between the villain and the heroine. He says to her, 'You had a mother,' and she says, 'I never had;' and then he says, 'You stole her will,' and she says, 'I never did.' There's lots of other talk in this scene, but that's the gist of it. Well, they search her and find the will. This naturally leads them to suspect the butcher, because he's a curate, so the detective arrests him again, and it's very exciting when he says he's innocent, and calls on the pawnbroker to say so too, and the pawnbroker says he can't tell a lie, because he's a bishop.

"So the curate, who is also a butcher, gets another seven years, and this prevents his coming into his title—he turns out to be a baronet. I forgot to mention that. Unfortunately, however, his father, who was a very careless man, forgot to copyright the title, and while he was in gaol it was barred by the Statute of Limitations—that's a novel situation.

"Then there enters the woman the villain has committed bigamy with. There's only one woman, but he has committed bigamy by marrying her twice, she being alive at the time of her second marriage with him. This gives rise to an ingenious complication. When the villain is confronted with her, he says, 'Curse her;' so they curse her, and she goes off 'left.'

"The heroine, however, who has succeeded in mesmerising herself, follows her into a lonely wood and stabs her with the penknife the curate uses when he's a butcher. Suspicion naturally falls on the curate, who is still in gaol, and he gets another seven years. Joe Giles, who is a comic servant, and has been in it all through, comes up just before she dies. She tries to tell him her dread secret— the secret of her life—but, to her horror, finds she can't remember it.

"After Giles has buried her he searches for the villain, finds him, and says, 'There he stands.' As the villain happens to be sitting down, he isn't believed, and is just about to be arrested for perjury, when the family solicitor comes in and says that as his aunt is now dead his lips are unsealed, and he may at last speak the truth. (That's novel. Did I mention he was a solicitor?) Yes! he may at last speak the truth. So he tries, but can't, and in this way it all comes out. The curate throws off his disguise as butcher, and gets seven years for personation.

"The heroine is so disgusted with all of them that she marries a man who wasn't in the play at all.

"At last the solicitor, after many futile attempts, succeeds in speaking the truth —and this brings down the curtain."

Jellicoe stopped.

"Well?" he said.

I looked out of the window.

"It's much clearer," I replied.

"The plot?"

"No! The weather."

"But the plot, old man," persisted Jellicoe. "Do you think it's good?"

"Good!" I answered. "Good is not the word;" and I went out into the rain.

THE BILLS.

INTRODUCTION.

HERE the writer gives his celebrated imitation of himself—imitating Sir Henry Irving in his well-known recital of Edgar Allan Poe's poem "The Bells."

As a rule it is not very like Irving, but it is very good of the reciter—to do it. Before reciting this piece it is desirable to take a few lessons from some professor of elocution, in order that the reciter who fails may have somebody to blame.

Here they come !—the Christmas Bills !
   Awful Bills !
And as they come, with blank despair
   My wretched bosom thrills.
How they flutter, flutter, flutter
Through the letter-box at door,
And my thoughts I dare not utter,
Save to groan in voiceless mutter,
   " Heavens ! are there any more ?"
   And they pour ! pour ! pour !

THE BILLS.

In the letter-box at door,
And they tumble on the floor,
As the letter-box it fills
Full of Bills! Bills! Bills! Bills!
Bills! Bills! Bills!

NOTE.—The reciter must be careful to say "Bills"
seven times exactly, and dwell on each repe-
tition.

Here—the year's provision Bills!
Butcher's Bills! baker's Bills!
And each appalling item gives my spinal
column chills.
Bacon, bread, and chops and steaks,
Legs of lamb, and currant cakes;
And I try but can't remember,
On the fourth of last September
Eating thirteen currant cakes.
And I try and try again,
While the baker sits and gloats.
Well he knows 'tis all in vain;
Well he knows I keep no notes.
Ah! the Bills! Bills! Bills!
How they swell,
As I dwell
On the future! Who can tell?
Can I ever?—shall I never
Pay those Bills! Bills! Bills! Bills!
Bills! Bills! Bills!

NOTE.—If the reciter finds difficulty in counting
the seven repetitions of "Bills" he may check
them off on his fingers.

Here—the local plumber's Bills!
Brazen Bills!
And with an awestruck terror now my
wretched bosom thrills.

THE BILLS.

In the dark ear of the night
How I shriek with mad affright
At the items in the local plumber's
    Bills !
Charging Time ! Time ! Time !
Without reason ! without rhyme !
Too much horrified to speak,
1 can only shriek and shriek
In a clamorous appealing to the mercy of
    the plumber,
In a mad expostulation with that fearsome
    local plumber !
Mounting higher ! higher ! higher !
And I have but one desire.
And a resolute endeavour,
That I'll never pay ! no never !
Oh ! the Bills ! Bills ! Bills !
The discord and the jangling caused
    by Bills !
Oh ! the discord and the wrangling,
When the Bills come in for mangling !
Oh ! the fearful rows and rackets
Caused by Bills for hats and jackets !
And the feathers and the frills !
And the Bills ! Bills ! Bills ! Bills !
    Bills ! Bills ! Bills !

NOTE.—If the audience be not exhausted, the
reciter may here venture on an extra "Bills."

AUTHOR'S NOTE.—It was here my intention to write
a verse about gas bills, but when I tried I found
I got too many cubic feet in some of the lines.
I have since discovered that this was due to
my using a defective metre.

Hear the ringing of the Bells !
Tradesmen's Bells !

THE BILLS.

Ah! what a world of solemn thought their
    monody compels!
      In the chilly winter night
      How I shiver with affright
    At the melancholy menace of their
      tone!
    And I groan
As the butcher and the baker and the coat
    and waistcoat maker
      Stand and ring!
      They are neither brute nor human!
      They are neither man nor woman!
      Let them ring!
    But the plumber is the king!
  And he Rings! Rings! Rings! Rings
    The back and front door bells,
    And his merry bosom swells,
    Charging Time! Time! Time!
    Without Reason, without Rhyme.
    Time for calling for his Bills!
For his unreceipted Bills! Bills! Bills!
    Bills! Bills! Bills! Bills!
  Bills! Bills! Bills! Bills! Bills! Bills
    Bills!

HALLO! WHAT ARE YOU DOING HERE?

In this vale of tears, where all pleasures
    are fleeting,
The boringest bore I am constantly meet-
    ing
Is he who comes up with this unfailing
    greeting—
      Hallo! what are *you* doing here?
I meet him in church, in a pub or
    the*ay*ter,
The North or South Pole, or upon the
    Equator,
The more likely the place, his surprise is
    the greater.
      Hallo! what are *you* doing here?

To the Island of Wight in the summer
    I'm sailing,
Head over the side, as one does when
    one's ailing,
When up comes my friend with his
    greeting unfailing—
      Hallo! what are *you* doing here?
I reply—" Come and look for your own
    satisfaction."

He does so. But such is the fatal attrac-
tion,
That shortly he's suiting the word to the
action.
>   Hallo! what is *he* doing here?

He calls at your own private house, and
he knows it,
You think he'll expect you'll be *there*.
Don't suppose it.
You appear. He is lost in amazement,
and shows it.
>   Hallo! what are *you* doing here?
And when we've both quitted this life,
which is fleeting,
Whichever's the place that's arranged
for our meeting
My friend won't expect me. He'll give
me this greeting—
>   Hallo! what are you doing *here!*

SLEEP.

My name is Solomon Snoreham. I am
a middle-aged bachelor of independent
means. I don't require to work for my
living. My friends tell me that it's very
lucky for me that I don't, and I quite
agree with them. One of them said to
me the other day, "I say, Solomon, what
do you do all day ? Have you *any* indoor
or outdoor recreation?" I told him I
never go out because it tires me, and my
indoor recreations are to eat, drink, and
sleep. "Well," he inquired, "which is
your favourite recreation of the three ? "
"I don't know," I replied. I always give
that as my first answer to any question.
I never *do* know until I've had time to
think a bit. When he went away I tried
to go to sleep again, but I couldn't do it
for thinking. I don't think much as a
rule ; but there I was, with my eyes shut,
trying to think whether I would rather
eat, drink, or sleep. I thought until my
head ached, and finally decided that sleep
is the best indoor recreation, and my own
particular choice. I have a lot of reasons.

In the first place, you can't overdo it—
at least, *I* can't. You may eat to excess,
and you may drink to excess, but you

can't sleep to excess. You may force yourself to eat when you're not hungry, and to drink when you're not thirsty, but you cannot sleep when you're not sleepy. I have made myself terribly ill by eating and drinking too much; but however much I sleep (and I sleep a good deal), I never feel any ill effects whatever.

Secondly: it passes away the time so nicely.

I may dawdle over my dinner from six until eight, but it gets very wearisome work towards the end. Then, what am I going to do until my bedtime, which is eleven o'clock prompt? I can't go on eating and drinking without disastrous results. No! I've more sense than that. I sit down in my armchair and have a sleep. In this way two, three, or even four hours may pass like five minutes, and when I awake it's bedtime, and I haven't felt bored all evening. A great advantage that sleep has in my eyes is, that it's no exertion. I hate exertion. I sleep without the slightest effort, and I'm sure it must suit me, for I never get tired of it, and I never feel tired after it.

Thirdly: I like it because I'm very good at it.

Every man likes doing what he does well, and sleeping is *my* strong point. I hear people say, "I couldn't sleep last night;" or, "I slept very, very badly." I pity them and feel superior. I can always sleep, day or night, and I sleep *well — very well indeed.* I never slept badly in my life. I should be ashamed of myself if I did. Whatever is worth doing is worth doing well, and if it is worth while to sleep it is a great shame to do it badly. I'm not very clever, and there are many accomplishments in which other men shine more than I do, but when it comes to sleeping I defy them all. The man who is not clever is just as good as the man who is clever when they're both asleep, and if he is the better sleeper he is the better man of the two.

I really think, as a healthy indoor recreation, sleep should be more encouraged. Why, the very word "recreation" suggests sleep. "Nature's sweet restorer (or re-creator), sleep." My doctor strongly recommends it. He says that so long as a man is awake, his brain-tissue is constantly wearing out, and that sleep renews it. He also adds, for my own private benefit, "As you haven't very much brain-tissue to work upon, you require a lot of sleep." Yes ; I finally maintain that, although as an outdoor pastime sleep has its drawbacks, as a purely indoor recreation it has neither flaw nor defect.

My doctor has just called, and I've told him my thoughts. He quite agrees with me, but looks grave, and says I shall require a lot of sleep to make up for such an unusual waste of brain-tissue. This is alarming. I'm off to bed at once. Good-night !

HOW TO ENJOY THE THEATRE.

I WAS once privileged to hear a lecture by a celebrated dramatist on the subject of "How to be Rightly Amused at the Theatre."

It occurred to me that the lecturer did not strike at the root of the matter, and that, before we discuss "how to be *rightly* amused," we ought to understand thoroughly "how to be amused at all." .

As for their full enjoyment the different forms of theatrical entertainment require different treatment, it may be as well to enumerate them to begin with.

There are three or four primary classes, each one of which is shaded into the other by means of a series of variations.

For instance, opera is shaded off into burlesque by means of "opera bouffe," "comic opera," &c. Burlesque slips imperceptibly into pantomime, and pantomime into the variety show. Tragedy moves through drama to melodrama ; and comedy, by easy stages, from farcical comedy to pure farce.

In order to thoroughly enjoy all these various forms, each one must be taken individually and treated according to its requirements.

It is not within the power of an audience to alter the form of the entertainment, but it is within the power of every individual member of that audience to alter his or her own conditions in order to suit the entertainment.

Therefore it is very desirable that audiences should create, within themselves, an artificial, temporary condition regulated according to the class of entertainment they happen to be attending.

Consider a few illustrations. We will begin with burlesque. The best time to enjoy a burlesque is after a good dinner, where there has been sufficient wine consumed to cause the delusion that the libretto is smart and the music tuneful. It is really wonderful what a different influence bad puns and weak jokes exert over the same minds under different conditions.

Let any man try to retail in the morning the best and wittiest thing he heard in the smoke-room last night over his sixth whisky.

It is flat—a lamentable failure—and he says feebly to the audience who should have laughed, but didn't, " Of course, I can't tell it like Jones did. We all roared at it last night."

No doubt they did, but the cause was not the subtle humour of Jones's story, nor yet the comic powers of Jones himself. The cause was the condition of the audience.

Therefore, the time to see a burlesque is after a good dinner, and the worse the burlesque the more wine will be necessary.

If these precautions are taken, no entertainment of this description can possibly fail.

Tragedy requires different treatment. Wine would be fatal to the enjoyment of any tragedy. Wine and tragedy in combination create sleep.

To thoroughly enjoy tragedy, the mind must be excited, the body asceticised. I recommend one or two cups of strong black coffee, and total abstinence from food for some hours previous to the performance. A seat in the pit (without back preferred), a critical knowledge of the play superior to that possessed by the performers, and an austere demeanour, will complete the enjoyment.

As regards applause—leave that to the unthinking portion of the audience. They like to cheer when they feel dull, which is generally after a long soliloquy by the principal actor.

* * * *

Touching melodrama, I have consulted the lady who cleans out my offices, and she unhesitatingly votes for " Gin and the Gallery."

She votes for gin because it is a good liquor to " cry on." She says that is why they always have a plentiful supply at well-managed funerals. She believes in the gallery because in that part of the house alone melodramatic souls congregate, and she finds it a greater pleasure to weep in company than alone. I believe my respected char-lady is quite right. To sit through a whole melodrama and enjoy it, you must be emotional. If you are not naturally emotional, you must supply the deficiency by artificial means, such as gin. Unless you do this you had far better remain at home.

I know a newspaper critic (a most abandoned critic) who was induced to try personally the effect of this artificial emotion on a new melodrama.

He was naturally a hard-hearted man, so that it took the best part of two bottles to get him in a proper frame of mind, but the result was eminently satisfactory. He went to scoff, but remained to weep.

He told me afterwards that it was a delightful sensation, the only drawback being the terrible reaction and violent headache he suffered from next morning.

*　　*　　*　　*

Opera requires rather more delicate handling. The element of romance must be present if an opera is to be thoroughly enjoyed.

Unfortunately, the average man of the world has this element knocked out of him at an early age, and this being so, artificial means must again be resorted to.

It is not good for man to be alone—at least not at an opera.

Every male opera-goer must be accompanied by a lady. He must take a strong personal interest in her *pro tem.*—and she must not be a relation.

I have nothing further to add to this advice, except that, in order to prevent misapprehension, it is better to make a point of never taking the same lady twice.

*　　*　　*　　*

There are some further types of theatrical performance on which I frankly confess myself unable to give reliable advice.

One is the "hotch-potch" of everything, commonly called the "musical play." It is in this play that the daughter sings to the weeping mother—

> "Ah, mother dear, dispel your grief,
> A song and dance will bring relief,"

and thereupon followeth the song and dance.

I believe this class of play was invented in America, and possibly American audiences have found out for themselves the best way to grapple with it and extract enjoyment from it.

I cannot see, however, how any audience can possibly enjoy a play that is by turns melodrama, farce, burlesque, tragedy and comedy — everything by turns and nothing long.

It changes its conditions more rapidly than the audience can change theirs. No man, however energetic, can undergo a burlesque preparation, and then, when the melodrama stop is turned on, raise the artificial necessary emotion to order and at once. There would be disastrous results if he were to try.

*   *   *   *

Another class of dramatic entertainment which it is difficult for me to imagine under favourable conditions is the amateur performance.

I have tried (Heaven knows *how* I have tried) to enjoy an entertainment of this description, but without success. I have had strong inducements to look favourably upon it. I have seen ladies act, in whom I had a strong personal interest of a temporary nature, and yet I have derived no pleasure. Of course, I have told them a very different tale at the time, but this is the free and irresponsible truth.

There was once I came very near to enjoying an amateur performance. It was when I myself was taking part in it. It really seemed to me that it had gone very well indeed, ever so much better than any performance I had seen before.

All my personal friends told me that it was the best show *they* had ever seen, and that "I was awfully good, quite the best character in the piece."

But a personal stranger whom I met a day or two later, and who did not recognise me as having been a performer, confided to me such an open and candid opinion of the performance in general, and of *my* performance in particular, that it was forced upon me that our performance was no better than the average, and that mine was considerably worse.

I thanked the personal stranger, and have ever since that day strictly confined myself to criticism.

I can only suppose that amateur performances are not intended for purposes of enjoyment—that is, so far as the audience is concerned. They are organised for purposes of charity only. Therefore let us bear with them, suffer under them, lie about them, and be charitable also.

*　　　*　　　*　　　*

I trust that these few hints to theatregoers will be taken in the spirit in which they are offered, and if but one solitary individual shall, by acting upon them, spend in pleasure a couple of hours that would otherwise have been passed in dulness, I shall feel they have not been written altogether in vain.

Hech, man, the noo! Hoo's a' wi' ye?
    Hoo's a' wi' ye the day?
Man! Hae ye heard the news aboot the
    Reverend McBrae?
Ye've no heard tell? Hoots! Man!
    Hoot! Toot!
        Ye havering, graceless loon!
Come ben the noo, and hae a crack! Sit
    doon, ye gowk, sit doon!
And whaur's your muckle sneeshin? And
    ye'll mayhap hae a—sup.
(I want to tell this tale in Scotch, if I can
    keep it up.)
The Reverend McBrae, ye ken's an unco'
    guid divine,
And gie's your hand, my trusty frien', and
    here's a hand o' mine.
(I don't mind telling you, as friends, I
    didn't write that line.
But running short o' Scotch, I worked it
    in for Auld Lang Syne.)
It's all aboot some drunken loons o'
    Edinburgh toon,
And hoo McBrae convertit them one
    braw, braw efternoon.
These loons were fond o' nips, and—no—
    it doesn't seem to fit.

I say ! Shall you object if I should mix
    it up a bit ?
Scotch shall occur in places, that you
    may depend upon,
I'll only talk in English when I'm stuck
    and can't get on.
You don't object ? I'm much obliged.
    I'll start the tale again.
It's called, " The Mission of McBrae to
    Drunken Scottish Men."

The Reverend McBrae was of a Calvin-
    istic turn,
And spurned all other Christians with a
    conscientious spurn.
He was broader in the body, on the
    whole, than in the mind,
And spent his life in trying to regenerate
    mankind.
His views respecting liquor were eccen-
    tric, for a Scot,
To judge from Scotsmen I have met,
    and I have met a lot,
He abominated whisky, which he called
    the " deevil's brew,"
I've never met a Scotsman who did that
    before. Have you ?
He cried : " Ma frien's, upon your chains
    ye forge anither link
The whiles ye tak' a half yin " (that is
    Scotch for " have a drink ").
But the Edinburgh laddies took their
    " half yins " and the risk,
And the Reverend McBrae found com-
    petition very brisk.

The streets are thronged with people, in
    the shops is goodly cheer,
For to-morrow is the very first of all the
    glad New Year.
And gaily flow the "half yins" and the
    "mutchkins" and the "nips,"
Enough, if stored collectively, to float a
    dozen ships :
For Edinburgh laddies drink the Auld
    Year oot, ye ken,
And then they drink the New Year in,
    like braw, braw Scottish men.
The Englishman who wants a drink, he
    hies him to a bar ;
The Scotsman has a simpler plan, and
    more effective far.
The Scotsman buys a bottle at a time, or
    maybe "twa."
"It's cheaper man, ye ken, and ye can
    drink where'er ye are.
It's waste o' siller buying nips and waste
    o' time to boot,
But when ye hae it on ye—well ! Here's
    tae ye, man ! Hoot ! Toot !"

The Reverend McBrae, of course, was not
    an idle man,
Amid this scene of revelry—he had an
    artful plan.
He hired a little mission-room, he hired
    dissolving views,
Ventriloquists, and other entertainers to
    amuse ;
He'd a magic lantern showing views of
    all the Holy Land,
Some vocalists, reciters, and a first-class
    German band.

He'd buns with currants in them, and, for
    liquor, coffee hot,
To lure in his teetotal web the whisky-
    loving Scot.
Although he advertised his show to start
    at half-past seven,
He hadn't got an audience by a quarter
    to eleven.
But, when McBrae is in despair, the boys
    come trooping in
About eleven o'clock or so, the evening to
    begin.
Ventriloquists ventriloquise, and tenors
    sweetly sing,
Dissolving views dissolve, and—well—
    the usual sort of thing,
Young ladies hand the currant buns to
    each expectant Scot,
And every one is served all round with
    coffee—coffee hot.
And every Scottish laddie pulled his
    whisky oot, ye ken,
And he poured it in his coffee, and they
    drank like Scottish men.
They blessed McBrae on such a nicht to
    gie them such a treat,
For whisky hot, ye ken, is warmer far
    than whisky neat.
And when the constant nipping took its
    usual effect
They entertained McBrae with songs
    you'd hardly call select.

McBrae remarked : "Aweel, my frien's,
    I think we'll just gang hame " ;
But ne'er a Scottish laddie could he get to
    think the same.

Says Jock : "I'm no convertit yet, what
    say ye, ma frien' John ?"
And John replied : " Weel ! hardly quite !
    But still I'm getting on."
And so this sort of thing went on till
    nearly half-past three,
When every Scottish laddie had a
    "drappie in his e'e."

In vain McBrae remarked his entertain-
    ment now was done.
They only answered : " Maybe so, but
    ours has just begun."
So in the end, the bobbies came from
    each surrounding beat,
Took each converted Scottish lad and
    threw him in the street.

And at the Court next day, ye ken,
    McBrae had to appear
For organising orgies on the last day of
    the year.
They fined him eighty saxpences, and noo
    McBrae just swears
That loons may sup just where they like
    or *when* for all he cares.

THE SAME OLD DRESS.

EDWIN would a-wooing go, tired of single
    life,
Angelina has no beau—says she'll be his
    wife—
Edwin says : " When once we're wed, all
    your heart can choose—
Dresses, jewels, shall be yours—nothing
    I'll refuse."
  Sweet Angelina's satisfied,
  Off to the church—a blushing bride,
  She wore a dress of purest white,
  Of most expensive make.
'Twas Edwin's little present, and she
    wore it for his sake.
  " With all my goods I thee endow,"
  Said Edwin, and he added : " Now
You'll never know what 'tis to want a
    new silk dress."

Time goes on, as time will do—trousseau's
    wearing out—
Edwin will be glad to buy plenty more,
    no doubt.
Angelina wants a dress—Angelina's sad—
Edwin says he can't afford—trade is very
    bad.

" And, if you *must* go to the ball,
Go in your old one, then, that's all ! "
She wore a dress of purest white,
So sweetly trimmed with green,
It really looked as good as new, since it
    had been to clean.
But all the ladies said : " Dear me !
I never did ! " and " Don't you see ?
She's actually wearing yet the old white
    dress ! "

Edwin alters more and more—trade is
    growing worse—
Angelina wants the cash—Edwin keeps
    the purse—
Angelina's eldest son's worn out all his
    clothes—
Edwin cannot understand where all the
    money goes.
Discussion keen, and Edwin wild—
Christening-robe for youngest child—
It wore a robe of purest white,
All covered up with lace.
It came in very handy, altered just to fit
    the case ;
But though 'twas very well disguised,
Yet somehow it was recognised,
And people said : " A useful thing—that
    old white dress."

Angelina growing old—dress no longer
    fits,
Wants a summer bonnet now—cudgelling
    her wits.
Never goes to Edwin, though ; 'tisn't any
    good,

He can never spare the cash—wouldn't if
    he could.
  In corner-shop, exposed to view,
  Second-hand clothes as good as new
  There hangs a dress that once was white,
  But now is white no more.
And all the ladies say: "Aha! we've
    seen that dress before."
  And when on Angelina's head
  They saw the bonnet, neighbours said :
"She's bought her summer bonnet with
    the old white dress."

THE PUBLIC ANALYST.

THERE lived a Public Analyst, no matter
    where or when,
Who was the most annoying, disagree-
    able of men.
He accepted invitations from his friends
    to go and dine,
And stated, impolitely, there was logwood
    in the wine,
The melted-butter, margarine—the mutton
    far from good,
And quite condemned the cod-fish as unfit
    for human food.
He analysed the whole menu. He swore
    the cream was chalk,
And found a trichinosis germ within the
    leg of pork.
Until his hosts, with one accord, just
    struck him off the list,
And so he had to dine alone, this Public
    Analyst.

And every day the Analyst still more ex-
    clusive grew ;
He daily found bacteria, original and
    new ;
He found them in his pudding and he
    traced them in his meat,

And he finally concluded that it wasn't
    safe to eat.
He inspected filtered water through a
    powerful microscope,
And when he saw the reptiles there,
    abandoned every hope.
He felt it was U. P. with him, and he
    as good as dead,
When reptiles swarmed in water, and
    bacteria in bread.
And then the City Coroner scored one
    upon his list,
And sent a jury round to analyse the
    Analyst.

And then they argued as to what the
    verdict was to be,
They suggested 'twas starvation in the
    twenty-first degree ;
They found the Public Analyst had nothing
    left inside,
And, since he couldn't live that way—well,
    that was why he died.
The Coroner maintained 'twas suicide as
    clear could be,
Committed in a state of permanent in-
    san*itee.*
But, in the end, they all agreed, and thus
    the verdict ran :
The Analyst has died—because—there's
    nothing in the man.
So, all you Public Analysts, take warning
    now by this,
And try to earn, before you die, a good
    analysis.

THE BANDIT CHIEF.

I HOLD the important position of prompter to the "Yorkshire Thespians," and the "Yorkshire Thespians" are actors of whom Yorkshire is proud. We act, not for money, but for fame. In other words we are amateurs in the strictest sense of the term. It must not, however, be supposed for a moment that we refrain from acting for money because we doubt our ability. Not at all. We are, to a member, fully convinced that our histrionic powers are of great pecuniary value, but, preferring to preserve our amateur status, we nobly waive our right to lucre, and are content with glory. With this latter commodity we are, so to speak, covered.

When the committee met a short time ago, for the purpose of deciding upon the next piece for representation, they were quite at a loss what to select. We seemed to have exhausted everything worthy of our powers, and, like Alexander, sighed for new worlds to conquer. Revivals of past successes were out of the question with a progressive society such as ours, and the writings of the present race of dramatists were not considered worthy of our talents. It was a happy thought of the stage manager that hit upon an old-fashioned melodrama entitled "The Bandit Chief."

The stage manager, I may here explain, is a retired army doctor. He is a good all-round man ; that is, the doctors say he is a good actor, and the actors say he is a good doctor.

In "The Bandit Chief" the opportunities for indulging in scenery and bloodshed were unlimited. This powerful play was written in 1762 or 1672—I forget which. Jacks (our comic man) asserted after the performance that the jokes must have been written B.C. 1762 ; but he was biassed, as will be seen hereafter. It was a splendid example of the old school— bristling with fights, murders, and general excitement. The language was magnificent. Every character expressed his or her views at great length, and in the "Ha ! sayest thou so ?" style. All the male characters went through the piece armed to the teeth, and deaths were so frequent that, after reading a page or two, one feared that the *dramatis personæ* could hardly hold out for thirty-six pages in the face of such an abnormal death-rate. Of course this was, as a matter of fact, no slight drawback to the "Thespians," the quantity of the stock company being much inferior to its quality ; but by a judicious doubling and trebling of characters (no man had less than two parts, and one man had five), that difficulty was overcome.

The rehearsal went off, much as rehearsals *generally* went off—neither better nor worse. The "Thespians" were, however, peculiar in one respect. They were so talented that they had a sublime contempt for rehearsals. They attended perfunctorily, as being the usual thing to do, but that was all.

Then came the night of the performance, and with it the audience. I, as prompter to the society, was at my post, and duly rang up the curtain within the usual half-hour after the advertised time.

The stage manager had been cast for the part of "The Bandit Chief." This bold outlaw was supposed to be of Italian nationality, with a strong strain of gipsy blood running in his veins. The doctor had, therefore, anointed himself with some dark pigment of his own manufacture—the principal ingredient of which was glue. This was unfortunate, because it was discovered when too late that everything he touched stuck to him. This drawback brought about the first catastrophe. It occurred soon after the rise of the curtain, when the Bandit Chief, after patting his son "Taraxacum," affectionately on the head—withdrew his hand with the wig attached. The audience had been very quiet up to this point, but woke up and laughed heartily at the incident, after which there was never a dull minute.

The first death was most successful.

The embryo corpse was a gentleman who, being possessed of a large amount of sound common sense, declined, when shot, to fall flat upon his back, as was the reckless method of the more enthusiastic. So he evolved the plan of standing with his back to a solid support, and when the fatal wound was given sliding gently and gracefully to the ground. There was some delay in his execution. The assassin's pistol (not being so murderously inclined as the assassin) refused to explode although snapped with great vehemence. The victim, after waiting his decease for several minutes with exemplary patience, unfortunately got on the slide, and not being able to arrest his progress reached the ground and died in good style. The pistol—evidently seeing that the man was dead anyhow, and that it could not be held responsible—then condescended to go off. This met with high approval from the audience, who " encored " the incident vigorously. The actors did not, however, acknowledge this just tribute to their powers.

The army was a great feature. It was a model army—an army that even Germany might envy. It was but small—only four strong—but nothing discouraged it. It was bruised, beaten, wounded, and even killed, but it came up smiling in fresh clothes five minutes after. It was actually decimated in the first act, through an unfortunate blunder. When in pursuit of the Bandit Chief, this daring outlaw (according to stage directions) fired, and killed one soldier (or a quarter of the army) before he was overpowered. Each member of the army was partial to dying, and (without consulting his fellows) each had made up his mind that he was the one to be killed. Such a self-sacrificing army it was! When the fatal shot was heard, the whole quartette fell, apparently pierced through their respective hearts. At the unique spectacle of one small pistol bullet causing such immense slaughter, the delight of the audience knew no bounds. Laughter, applause, and cries of "Good shot!" rang through the hall. The army, actuated by one impulse, realising that if all died there would be nobody to arrest the prisoner, rose as one man, looked at each other, and then all fell down again. The curtain followed their example, and Act I. concluded amid such expressions of delight as had never before reached the ears of the "Yorkshire Thespians."

The remaining acts were so full of incident that it is impossible to do more than give a brief summary. The Bandit Chief, whose capture by the military was the chief motive of the play, was often put to sore straits to prevent his pursuers from seeing and being obliged to capture him before the last act. On one occasion, through defective stage management, Captain Potlion stumbled on him unexpectedly. Did he betray him to his men? No! Perish the thought!

Realising that this treachery on his part would bring the play to an untimely end, 'he gallant captain not only held his peace, but, indicating to the unhappy fugitive his nearest exit, bowed him out with an amiable smile, and then exclaimed in the words of his part : " Come ! it is useless seeking further, we are again foiled, and the bird has flown ! "

The audience did not allow this noble conduct to pass without expressing their audible (very audible) appreciation.

The only man who met with neither applause nor laughter was poor Jacks, the comic man. His part was full of very funny lines, of jokes that had stood the test of time, and we had all looked to him to infuse a good deal of humour into the piece. But no ! he was a dead failure. The only laughs he got were when he did something stupid and unintentional. When one of the numerous villains should have locked him in a room, but by an oversight made his exit leaving the door wide open, Jacks might have got out of his difficulty by some more graceful means than ostentatiously fastening the door himself, and then exclaiming in horror " Heavens ! I am a prisoner ! "

Again, when he declared his intention of going down a well of unfathomable depth, and sat on the brickwork before descending, it was very careless of him to drop the bucket into the unknown depths; of course it banged on the stage in such a manner as to entirely dispel the illusion. He did even worse though, when, after lowering himself with elaborate caution, he sat on the stage and allowed a leg to protrude visibly on each side of the well.

I was sorry for him, because he is a decent fellow, and a painfully conscientious actor. I *have* heard him described as more painful than conscientious, but that was by a newspaper critic, and newspaper critics will say anything. I, as prompter, had been kept very busy throughout the piece. In addition to keeping the actors on their lines, it was my duty to make all the outside noises. As nearly every other line in the play demanded something of the sort, I got somewhat fatigued towards the end of the third act. I had screamed " Help ! " I had shouted " Kill him ! " I had dropped planks to cover up deficient pistol reports, I had thundered, lightened, rained, hailed, sung like a woman, marched like an army, and howled like an "infuriated rabble inflated by drink." On the top of all this the Bandit Chief, who, in consequence of being pursued and shot at for two long acts, was in a state of high excitement, gave out his lines: " I hear the Count returning with his hounds from the chase," and then, sidling towards me at the wings, exclaimed in a fierce *sotto voce :* "Bark, you fool—bark ! Why the dickens don't you bark ? "

Well, I'm a poor barker, but I did my best, and he needn't have been so nasty about it. The audience enjoyed it, if he didn't. In fact there was a loud call for the " bull pup," but stage etiquette and a fear of causing needless jealousy restrained me from going on to acknowledge the compliment.

The Count caused great consternation

just as the curtain was going up on the last act, by announcing his fixed intention of "chucking it," and going home. He said "he believed the audience were 'guying' the whole thing, and he'd be 'blest if he'd stand it any longer.'" The stage manager's arguments, prayers and threats were unavailing, and it was not until the prettiest girl in the company took him in hand, and told him what flattering remarks she'd heard about him from her friends in the audience during the interval that he consented to play to the end, remarking, "Well, really, Miss Jones, if *you* say so, it's all right, but it's very funny that they should always laugh at my curses."

Well, we played it to the end—that is, all but Jacks. This unfortunate comedian was reduced to such a state of incompetency and drivelling idiocy by the audience's lack of interest in him that when he was asked in stage language, "Who art thou?" he feebly responded "I don't know," and retired to be seen no more.

The Bandit Boy (Taraxacum) was thrown into the raging torrent by hired assassins, and, after some twenty minutes (presumably spent in fancy swimming, or a game of Water Polo) condescended to call for "help." The Bandit Chief ascended the bridge, whispered to Taraxacum (plainly visible to the audience) to stand clear and then jumped into the raging torrent with a dull thud, that induced all to believe he had broken through two or three feet of solid ice. Rescuer and rescued duly reappeared amidst deafening cheers, quite dry and apparently healthy. Only apparently, however, for the Bandit Chief, after a long and impassioned speech, died in great agony from some mysterious disease of which he had shown no previous signs. Taraxacum was restored to his mother (the Countess) and nothing remained but the arrest of the villainous Count. This should have been accomplished by the army, led on by the comic man, but this unfortunate gentleman having dressed and retired to the bosom of his family, as before explained, the army remained at the wings. The villain, therefore, after delivering his last line—" Hell's curses on you all ! " with much fervour, retired, a free man, and with all his fearful crimes unexpiated. Then the curtain fell, and a terrific recall showed the "Yorkshire Thespians" that all their previous triumphs must pale before this, their latest and greatest.

One of our leading supporters in the audience came round at the fall of the curtain and congratulated us heartily.

"It was a splendid idea of you fellows," he said, " to advertise a melodrama and then give us a burlesque. It was a lovely little surprise, and we *have* enjoyed it. You all acted splendidly, except Jacks. He was very poor, but all the rest of you were too funny for anything."

We kept our own counsel. If an audience is so dense as to think a melodrama is a burlesque, it must wallow in its ignorance. Our duty is to act, not to supply intelligence. We are going to play a real burlesque soon. Perhaps they'll mistake that for a tragedy. Who knows?

THE DEAN WHO GAVE HIMSELF AWAY.

You'll find that Little Slumberton is
    marked upon the map;
At least, on any map that, as a map, is
    worth a rap.
But Slumberton's position as a geographic
    spot—
Well, that's a point on which conflicting
    evidence is hot.
The gentlemen who travel, and whose
    pace of life is fast,
Say of all created places Little Slumber-
    ton's the last.
But the infant Slumbertonian's instructed
    from his birth
That Slumberton's position is the centre
    of the earth.
And, as his mind develops, in his brain
    this fact resolves—
That Slumberton's the axis upon which
    the earth revolves.

    .   .   .   .

The Slumbertonian natives are a patriotic
    race,
They admire themselves extremely and
    adore their native place,
They possess a splendid workhouse and
    an ornamental park;

THE DEAN.

They have brewers of distinction, also
    clergymen of mark,
With a Mayor and Corporation, but, above
    all men, I ween, .
The Little Slumbertonians are proudest of
    their Dean.

       .   .   .   .

The Very Reverend the Dean of Little
    Slumberton
Is round and sleek, benevolent, and fair
    to look upon,
With records of a blameless life he literally
    teems,
And, like a philanthropic sun, on Slumber-
    ton he beams.

       .   .   .   .

The Dean was in his library, revolving in
    his mind
Some philanthropic plans whereby to
    benefit mankind ;
In pious thought he sad absorbed, till
    suddenly aware
That a gentleman unknown to him was
    standing by his chair.
Now, were a stranger in your house so
    coolly to intrude,
I fancy you'd expostulate in language
    somewhat rude.
But since the very worthy Dean was
    better far than you,
He bowed politely, beamed, and said,
    " Dear friend, how do you do ? "
The stranger first apologised for ven-
    turing to call,
And hoped he'd not disturbed the Dean.
    The Dean said, " Not at all."

He begged him to be seated, and draw
    closer to the fire,
And offered him advice or help, if sucn
    were his desire.
All this was said in such a truly philan-
    thropic tone
As never could be equalled, saving by the
    Dean alone.

      .   .   .   .

The stranger was a sallow man, of rather
    under-size,
Somewhat bony as to figure, with a pair
    of cold, grey eyes.
He told the Dean he travelled for the
    firm of Smith and Green,
Who published every Saturday, "The
    Bookworm's Magazine."
His firm to him the pleasurable duty had
    assigned
Of writing weekly essays on "The Leaders
    of Mankind,"
So straightway he had hied him to the
    Dean of Slumberton
To entreat him to consent to sit for Leader
    Number One.

      .   .   .   .

The Dean he coughed a modest cough,
    and smiled a modest smile,
Was really much surprised that they had
    thought it worth their while,
Of course it was most flattering to think
    that he had been
Selected, as an article, in such a Magazine.
He hardly thought the world would care
    for aught that he could say,

But still, if they thought otherwise, he
    would not answer, " Nay."
And so the Dean objected, but with feeble
    argument,
Till, by dint of importunity, the stranger
    gained consent.

       .   .   .   .

And then the representative of Messrs.
    Smith and Green,
Proceeded, without more ado, to interview
    the Dean.
He asked the very reverend one to give
    him, year by year,
The record of his blameless life and
    purely bright career.
And, as the Dean laid bare his life from
    shortly after birth
The stranger took a pen and wrote "for
    all that he was worth."

       .   .   .   .

The Dean narrated how, when quite a
    weeny teeny boy,
Another boy had struck him, and had
    robbed him of a toy,
And how the robber's parents had intended
    to chastise,
But the injured one had pled for him, salt
    tears within his eyes.
He then recalled his school-days, all the
    prizes he had won,
The scores he'd made at cricket, and the
    races he had run,
He spoke of thrashings meekly borne
    because he wouldn't "tell,"
And said his mates adored him, and the
    masters loved him well.

But if little peccadilloes in his life had
 e'er occurred,
He surely had forgotten, for of them he'd
 ne'er a word.
And then he traced his college life, the
 midnight oil he'd burnt,
The useful lessons taught by him, the
 useful lessons learnt,
How, all through life, philanthropy had
 triumphed over pelf,
But—if he'd e'er done wicked deeds, he
 kept those to himself—
Till, weary of remembering, the Dean
 opined it best
That Smith and Green should call again
 to chronicle the rest.

  . . . .

The Dean sat in his library to smoke his
 evening pipe,
And fell to thinking how his life would
 look when set in type.
He thought the record of his life, as told
 to Smith and Green,
Should edify the readers of "The Book-
 worm's Magazine,"
But when he fell to pondering on what
 had just occurred,
He found he simply could not recollect a
 single word.
He'd surely done some noble deeds, but,
 be that so or not,
Although he tried his very best, could not
 remember what.
In place of recollections he had long
 looked back upon
There came unpleasant mem'ries to the
 Dean of Slumberton.

There were nasty, petty meannesses, and
    little acts of spite,
And thoughts of when he'd acted wrong
    instead of acting right.
He thought of canings he'd deserved and
    got while young at school,
He seemed to hear the master say, "That
    boy's a thorough fool."
He recollected stealing jam and toffee, ay,
    and worse.
He thought of how, in infant rage, he
    once had slapped his nurse.
" My memory is failing, I'm afraid," he
    softly said,
" And I'm really very sleepy, so I'll just
    get off to bed."

       .   .   .   .

The Dean was in his library exact at half-
    past ten,
With equal punctuality the stranger called
    again.
The worthy Dean of Slumberton had got
    his mem'ry back,
Of holy thoughts and gracious acts to-day
    he had no lack.
No worthy deed did he omit, nor worth-
    less action state,
And so he spun his yarn until he'd got it
    up to date.

       .   .   .   .

And when the Dean of Slumberton had
    nothing more to tell
The stranger rose, and rubbed his hands,
    remarked, " So far, so well.
There now is but one little thing that
    Smith and Green require.

Of course, I hardly need to say the public
will desire

To see the portrait of the Dean, so, for
the public's sake

No doubt you will allow me, sir, your
likeness now to take?"

And with a demon camera the stranger,
then and there,

Secured the likeness of the Dean while
sitting in his chair.

.   .   .   .

And here a marv'llous thing occurred.
Much to the Dean's surprise

He saw the stranger grow like him—the
Dean—before his eyes ;

And something said inside the Dean of
Little Slumberton

That now, alas, for ever, his identity was
gone.

.   .   .   .

And while he sat and marvelled much,
the awful stranger spoke :

" Ex-Dean, you've done a thing to-day
you never can revoke ;

The blameless record of your past you've
yielded unto me,

You've given me your likeness, as you
very plainly see ;

Your pleasant recollections you have given
all away,

And I propose to live as you henceforward
from to-day.

The memories you chose to keep ! Why !
those belong to you ;

You kept them to yourself, and those I
leave you for review :

Henceforth I am the Dean himself, as
    you were till to-day ;
While you go forth, a foolish man, 'who
    gave himself away.'"

    .   .   .   .

And now the stranger is the Dean of
    Little Slumberton ;
He's round and sleek, benevolent, and
    fair to look upon,
And Little Slumbertonians love their
    country and their Queen ;
But still, above all men on earth, they all
    adore their Dean.

    .   .   .   .

And he who was the Dean has nothing
    now on earth to do
But recollect his many sins, and virtues
    very few :
They don't know him in Slumberton, and
    that fact being so,
He cannot tell you who he is, and I'm
    sure I don't know.

H

PHRENOLOGY.

A NON-SCIENCICAL LECTURE.

SCENE.—*A Public Hall. On the platform a table, with water-bottle and glass. A phrenological chart on the wall. Six people in the audience who have come in with free tickets. Enter a Professor of Phrenology armed with a pointer, and amid faint applause.*

The PROFESSOR *speaks :—*

Ladies and Gentlemen,—Phrenology is a science. "Science" is derived from the German word "Scio," "I know."

That is the motto of the scientist who lectures. When he doesn't know, his motto is "Non-scio." His lecture is then "Non-science," or colloquially, "Nonsense." This, however, does not keep the scientist from lecturing. At least, it doesn't hinder me.

Were I to confine myself to-night to telling you what I know, my lecture would be brief and uninteresting. As it is, it will be lengthy and ignorant. I sincerely hope that my ignorance may be your bliss.

My non-sciencical subject is "Phreno

logy, or the investigation of the human head."

The human head is full of interest, even if it is empty of everything else. There are many kinds of heads—level-heads, long-heads, thick-heads, block-heads, and dead-heads.

This illustration *(pointing to Figure 1)* is a very fine speci-men of the "caput defunctus communis," or "common dead-head." This head is bald, but not unin-teresting. The lines and numbered spaces are not for the pur-pose of playing chess or shove ha'penny. They represent the compartments in

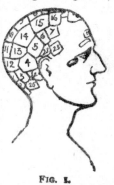

FIG. 1.

which the owner keeps his various forms of intellect.

It may be well to note here how this gentleman's ruling passion has affected the formation of his head. He has fre-quented theatre stalls to such an extent, and thought about them so constantly, that his brain has gradually assumed the appearance of the box office plan. You see here dramatic instinct, stern deter-mination, and rigid economy all well developed. This combination results in a fixed intention to go to the theatre as often as he can without paying.

Love of music—which should be here —is lacking. In its place, very pronounced, is the gift of thirst. This induces him, while the orchestra plays during the intervals, to go to the bar in search of drink. The stern determination and rigid economy noticed before make it a practical certainty that some one else will pay.

Love of literature is wanting, therefore he doesn't buy a programme. This large space is cheek—pure cheek. This space is keen appreciation. He generally shows his appreciation of the favour of a free ticket by asking for another one next day.

He is to be met with oftenest at unpopular or poor performances. This shows either lack of discrimination on his part, or sound judgment on the part of the theatrical manager.

We will now pass on to a more interesting and varied class of head.

This head (*Fig. 2*) is owned by a man of great force of character. It abounds

FIG. 2.

in bumps, or, as we phrenologists put it, is a thoroughly bumptious head.

Every head has bumps varying in size and number. They come in various ways. If you think very hard on one particular subject, your head swells in one particular place, and there's your bump.

PHRENOLOGY.

I know a gentleman who, one night, thought very hard for four hours to find a reasonable explanation that would satisfy his wife as to why he came home so late. During these four hours he thought of everything—simply everything—and, in the morning, found that his head had swelled so much all over that he couldn't get his hat on—and his wife didn't believe him after all.

It is a mistake to suppose that bumps are permanent, as this gentleman's case will prove. After the excitement caused by this amount of thought, a great reaction set in, during which all the bumps disappeared, and, in their place, succeeded a distinct and very great depression.

First, we have the bump of Puerilitativeness, or love of children. This is a peculiar bump. It subsides in proportion as your family increases. I have a case in my mind now of a gentleman who, before he was married, had this bump largely developed. Now he has fourteen children, and, where that bump was, there is a hollow about the size of a soup-plate. People who have this bump give other people's children a large amount of toffee. It may be fairly calculated that, for every eighteen-pennyworth of toffee given, the father pays a doctor's bill of three guineas. This reduces his bump materially, and, if he has the bump of admiration for doctors, that subsides also.

The next is a very dangerous bump— the bump of Generosability, or the desire to give away things. Unfortunately I have this myself, but I keep it in subjection by the constant application of melted butter. In spite of this precaution, however, I am constantly giving my friends away. I know a man who is greatly afflicted with this bump. He has given away eight daughters, and is anxious to give away four more. In fact, he finds it almost impossible even to keep himself.

The next bump is the bump of Humour. The happy possessor of this is able to enjoy a good joke. This bump must not be confused with the one called "extract of humour." This latter is possessed by many comedians, and enables them to extract all the humour out of a good joke, and leave nothing in it whatever. In the bump of humour lies the secret of popularity—that is, if you also have the great gift of silence. Add to these the bump of Veneration, which comes in useful for the old jokes, and the art of simulation (invaluable when you are not amused at all), and you are a good audience and a popular man.

The tip of the nose denotes colour. The dark patch under the eye denotes a quiet, peaceful nature. The fulness of the ear denotes music. The fulness of the neck—apoplexy. They are both gifts or diseases, according to circumstances. (Pointing.) This is treachery, and this is —a blot. This is literary debility, and this—pure cussedness—a lamentable combination. This is ambition; this is—a wart; this is resolution; these are his whiskers; and this concludes my lecture.

I shall now be happy to give advice to any gentleman as to the selection of a trade or profession.

Enter the SUBJECT.

Ah ! this gentleman *(the* PROFESSOR *feels the* SUBJECT'S *head)* would make a very good—bankrupt. Have you any idea yourself, sir, of what you would like to be ?

Subject. I would like to be an angel !

Professor. An angel ! A bankrupt angel ! An angel that has failed ! Well ; you might make a good stoker. You have a fiery nature.

Subject. No, I haven't.

Professor. But you have. **You are** naturally very impulsive.

Subject. No, I'm not !

Professor. I say you are ! The bump of impetuosity is just here.. I'll prove it. What'll you have to drink ?

Subject. Small Scotch.

Professor. There you are ! You see how impetuous you are ! You rush at things. Now, if I were as impulsive as you, I should very likely stand you one—but I'm not. There are here two large bumps— self-conceit and general incompetence.

Subject. I ought to make a good phrenologist then, oughtn't I ?

Professor. Well, no. They are hardly large enough for that. Now, let me see. Yours is a very peculiar head—most peculiar. Do you ever work ?

Subject. Only when I'm obliged.

Professor. Ah! Yet you are fond of work.

Subject. Passionately.

Professor. Very strange. Ah! Here is a very large bump—Imagination. I see. You like to sit still and think you're working, eh?

Subject. I do.

Professor. I thought so. Ah! here is generosity — very largely developed — amounting almost to a craze for lavish expenditure. This is very gratifying. My fee is—— How much money have you about you?

Subject. I haven't any.

Professor. No money?

Subject. None.

Professor. Then my advice to you is— go and earn some.

Subject. But what profession ought I to follow?

Professor. It really doesn't matter which you follow. You're not likely to overtake any of them.

Exit the SUBJECT.

Professor. I think, ladies and gentlemen, I will not, on these terms, waste any more of my valuable advice to-night.

Exit the PROFESSOR.

SOMETHING ORIGINAL.

THE poet was raving and tearing his hair
The poet despaired with the wildest
    despair,
For, had he not sworn an unbreakable
    swear
      He'd write something original !
So for long weary weeks he sat up in his
    bed,
And wrote little rhymes that came into
    his head,
They were sweet little verses, but every
    one said,
      They were *hardly* original.

He wrote verses that savoured of Shake-
    speare and Scott,
Of Chaucer and Cowper and all of that
    lot,
Very nice in their way ; but, alas ! they
    were *not*—
      They were *not* quite original.
Till one happy day he went out of his
    mind,
Developed a brain of a drivelling kind,
And now everybody's delighted to find
      That he's grown quite original

SOMETHING ORIGINAL.

He sits in his cell and he writes lovely
    verse
About glittering moons, and a gibbering
    curse,
Of the clanking of chains and the hypno-
    tised hearse—
        Oh !　So quaint and original !
Of the glimmering glamour and shimmer-
    ing sheen,
Of the hush of the corn and the bloom of
    the bean ;
And, though nobody yet has explained
    what they mean,
        Still, they are *quite* original.

WARD, LOCK & CO.'S

LILY SERIES

Crown 8vo. Beautifully bound in Cloth, with attractive pictorial design and Book Envelope in colour. Frontispiece also in colour.
2s. 6d. net.

The world changes—new times, new manners, new writers of books, new buyers of books—but there are certain old favourites the demand for which not only does not diminish, but tends steadily to increase. The Lily Series is designed to present such volumes in the most attractive modern form at the lowest possible price. Forty volumes now ready; many others in preparation.

(Continued on next page.)

WARD, LOCK & CO., LIMITED, LONDON, E.C.4.

WARD, LOCK & CO.'S

LILY SERIES

(Continued).

Crown 8vo. Beautifully bound in Cloth, with attractive pictorial design and Book Envelope in colour. Frontispiece also in colour. 2s. 6d. net.

23	THE SWISS FAMILY ROBINSON	—
24	THE LAMPLIGHTER	Miss Cummins
25	ERIC	F. W. Farrar
26	THE BASKET OF FLOWERS	G. T. Bedell
27	THE DOG CRUSOE	R. M. Ballantyne
28	DAISY	Elizabeth Wetherell
29	AT THE MERCY OF TIBERIUS	A. J. Evans Wilson
30	THE THREE MIDSHIPMEN	W. H. G. Kingston
31	DAISY IN THE FIELD	Elizabeth Wetherell
32	EAST LYNNE	Mrs. Henry Wood
33	BEULAH	A. J. Evans Wilson
34	BARRIERS BURNED AWAY	E. P. Roe
35	JOHN HALIFAX, GENTLEMAN	Mrs. Craik
36	THE GORILLA HUNTERS	R. M. Ballantyne
37	A RING OF RUBIES	Mrs. L. T. Meade
38	MACARIA	A. J. Evans Wilson
39	MONICA	E. Everett-Green
40	BEN-HUR	Lew Wallace
41	QUEECHY	Elizabeth Wetherell
42	JILL, A FLOWER GIRL	L. T. Meade
43	THE WORLD OF ICE	R. M. Ballantyne
44	THE CHANNINGS	Mrs. Henry Wood
45	MELBOURNE HOUSE	Elizabeth Wetherell
46	PETER THE WHALER	W. H. G. Kingston
47	A DWELLER IN TENTS	L. T. Meade
48	DANESBURY HOUSE	Mrs. Henry Wood
49	MARTIN RATTLER	R. M. Ballantyne
50	FROM JEST TO EARNEST	E. P. Roe

WARD, LOCK & CO., LIMITED, LONDON, E.C.4.

The Windsor Magazine

The Biggest Brightest and Best Illustrated Monthly

Ward · Lock · & · Co · Limited · London